A MOTHER'S LOVE LEDGER

This love ledger is for:

ISBN 978-0-692-13905-9

Designed by: M.Heckel Design
Printed by: Oh My Word Luxury Paperie

TheEncouragerPodcast.com

Hello!
Thank you so much for purchasing your Legacy Journal! Below are some thoughts to help with this awesome journey of leaving your legacy to your children through your personal, handwritten journal entries. I encourage you to start with thinking about:

- Milestones
- Funny moments
- Your child's favorite things, activities and quirks
- Prayer requests
- Quotes and Scriptures
- What you are working on with them to prepare them for life

Remember to record the date and any little details you want your child to remember. I try to journal once a week, but this book belongs to you – no pressure, no rules – simply do what is best for you, your family, and your stage of life.

Cheers to you fellow mama, we've got this!

Rebekah Scott

Date ____________________

Date ________________

Date ____________________

Date ___________________

Date ______________

Date ______________

Date ____________

Date ________________

Date ____________________

Date ______________

"Perhaps this is the moment for which you were created." **Esther 4:14**

Date ________________

Date ______________

Date

Date ______________

Date ____________________

Date ____________________

Date ____________________

Date ______________

Date ____________________

Date ______________

Date

Date ____________________

Date ______________

"Tell me and I forget, teach me and I may remember, involve me and I learn."
Benjamin Franklin

Date ____________________

Date ______________

Date ____________

Date ____________________

Date ______________

Date ______________________

Date ______________

Date ______________________

Date ____________

Date

Date ______________

"When I am afraid I will trust in You." **Psalm 56:3**

Date ______________

Date ______________

Date

Date ____________________

Date ______________

Date ________________

Date ____________________

Date

Date ____________

Date ______________

Date ________________

"For we are God's handiwork, created in Christ Jesus to do good works, which God prepared in advance for us to do." **Ephesians 2:10**

Date ______________

Date ____________________

Date ______________________

Date ____________________

Date ________________

Date ____________________

Date ____________________

Date ____________________

Date ___

Date ______________

Date ________________

Date ______________

Date ____________

"There is no way to be a perfect mother, but a million ways to be a good one."
Unknown

Date ______________

Date ____________________

Date ______________

Date ____________________

Date ____________________

Date ____________________

Date ________________

Date ____________________

Date ____________________

Date ______________

Date ____________________

Date ____________________

Date ______________

"The most precious jewels you'll ever have around your neck are the arms of your children." **Unknown**

Date ____________

Date ______________

Date ____________

Date ______________

Date ______________

Date ______________

Date ___

Date ____________________

Date ______________________

Date ____________

Date ______________

Date ______________

Date ___________________

Date ______________

Date ____________

"Be still and know that I am God." **Psalm 46:10**

Date ______________

Date ____________

Date ________________

Date ____________________

Date ____________

Date ____________________

Date ______________

Date ____________________

Date ______________

Date ____________________

Date ______________

Date

Date ______________

"Tell your mountain about your God." **Unknown**

Date ____________

Date ______________

Date

Date

Date ______________

Date ____________________

Date ______________________

Date ____________

Date

Date ______________

Date ______________

"You are far more precious than jewels." **Proverbs 31:10**

Date ______________

Date ______________

Date ______

Date ____________

Date ____________________

Date ___________________

Date ____________

Date ____________________

Date ____________________

Date

Date ____________

"Children are a heritage of the Lord, and the fruit of the womb is His reward."
Psalm 127:3

Date ____________________

Date ________________

Date

Date ______________

Date ____________________

Date ____________________

Date ____________________

Date ______________________

Date ___

Date ____________________

Date ___

Date ____________________

Date ______________

"As one whom his mother comforts, so I will comfort you." **Isaiah 66:13**

Date ____________

Date ______________

Date ________________

Date ______________

Date

Date ______________

Date ________________

Date ____________

Date ______________

Date ____________________

Date ____________________

Date ____________________

Date ______________

"For this child I have prayed." **1 Samuel 1:27**

Date ____________________

Date ____________

Date ____________

Date

Date ________________

Date ____________________

Date ______________

Date

Date ______________

Date ____________________

Date

REBEKAH SCOTT DESIGNS®

Rebekah@ShopRSD.com
ShopRSD
@ShopRSD

THE ENCOURAGER
WITH REBEKAH SCOTT

EncouragerPodcast
TheEncouragerPodcast.com